MW00636098

Gardening

The Gardener's Journal

Gardening adds years to your life
and life to your years.

The "*Write It Down!*"® Series
by Journals Unlimited, Inc.

Printed in the USA using recycled materials.

Life is an adventure

It's not the destination we
reach that's most rewarding.
It's the journey along the way.

So **Write It Down!** & treasure
the memory forever. . .

Barbara Morina

Common name:_____

Botanical name:_____

Purchased at:_____ Price:_____

☐ Annual　　☐ Perennial　　☐ Flower　　☐ Shrub　　☐ Tree

☐ Bareroot　☐ Groundcover　☐ Fruit　　☐ Vegetable　☐ Herb

Started from: ☐ Seed　☐ Plant

Date germinated:_____ Date planted:_____

Location planted:_____

Planting instructions:_____

_____

_____

Sunlight: ☐ Full sun　☐ Partial sun　☐ Shade

Water requirements:_____ Size at maturity:_____

Care instructions:_____

_____

_____

_____

_____

Fertilizer / soil amendment / herbicide:_____

_____

_____

Harvest / bloom date:_____

Transplant / propagate / divide:_____

_____

_____

Pests / problems:_____

_____

_____

_____

Notes:_____

_____

_____

_____

_____

_____

_____

_____

Photo / plant tag / seed packet / drawing:

Common name:_____

Botanical name:_____

Purchased at:_____ Price:_____

☐ Annual   ☐ Perennial   ☐ Flower   ☐ Shrub   ☐ Tree

☐ Bareroot   ☐ Groundcover   ☐ Fruit   ☐ Vegetable   ☐ Herb

Started from: ☐ Seed ☐ Plant

Date germinated:_____ Date planted:_____

Location planted:_____

Planting instructions:_____

_____

_____

Sunlight: ☐ Full sun ☐ Partial sun ☐ Shade

Water requirements:_____ Size at maturity:_____

Care instructions:_____

_____

_____

_____

_____

Fertilizer / soil amendment / herbicide:_____

_____

_____

Harvest / bloom date:_____

Transplant / propagate / divide:_____

_____

_____

_____

Pests / problems:_____

_____

_____

_____

© 1998 Journals Unlimited, Inc., Bay City, MI ™ "Write It Down" ® Series

Notes:_____

_____

_____

_____

_____

_____

_____

_____

Photo / plant tag / seed packet / drawing:

Common name:_____

Botanical name:_____

Purchased at:_____ Price:_____

☐ Annual   ☐ Perennial   ☐ Flower   ☐ Shrub   ☐ Tree

☐ Bareroot   ☐ Groundcover   ☐ Fruit   ☐ Vegetable   ☐ Herb

Started from: ☐ Seed   ☐ Plant

Date germinated:_____ Date planted:_____

Location planted:_____

Planting instructions:_____

_____

_____

Sunlight: ☐ Full sun   ☐ Partial sun   ☐ Shade

Water requirements:_____ Size at maturity:_____

Care instructions:_____

_____

_____

_____

_____

Fertilizer / soil amendment / herbicide:_____

_____

_____

Harvest / bloom date:_____

Transplant / propagate / divide:_____

_____

_____

_____

Pests / problems:_____

_____

_____

_____

Notes:_____

_____

_____

_____

_____

_____

_____

_____

Photo / plant tag / seed packet / drawing:

Common name:_____

Botanical name:_____

Purchased at:_____ Price:_____

☐ Annual   ☐ Perennial   ☐ Flower   ☐ Shrub   ☐ Tree

☐ Bareroot   ☐ Groundcover   ☐ Fruit   ☐ Vegetable   ☐ Herb

Started from: ☐ Seed   ☐ Plant

Date germinated:_____ Date planted:_____

Location planted:_____

Planting instructions:_____

_____

_____

Sunlight: ☐ Full sun   ☐ Partial sun   ☐ Shade

Water requirements:_____ Size at maturity:_____

Care instructions:_____

_____

_____

_____

_____

Fertilizer / soil amendment / herbicide:_____

_____

_____

Harvest / bloom date:_____

Transplant / propagate / divide:_____

_____

_____

_____

Pests / problems:_____

_____

_____

_____

_____

Notes:_____

_____

_____

_____

_____

_____

_____

_____

Photo / plant tag / seed packet / drawing:

Common name:_____

Botanical name:_____

Purchased at:_____ Price:_____

☐ Annual   ☐ Perennial   ☐ Flower   ☐ Shrub   ☐ Tree

☐ Bareroot   ☐ Groundcover   ☐ Fruit   ☐ Vegetable   ☐ Herb

Started from: ☐ Seed   ☐ Plant

Date germinated:_____ Date planted:_____

Location planted:_____

Planting instructions:_____

_____

_____

Sunlight: ☐ Full sun   ☐ Partial sun   ☐ Shade

Water requirements:_____ Size at maturity:_____

Care instructions:_____

_____

_____

_____

_____

Fertilizer / soil amendment / herbicide:_____

_____

_____

Harvest / bloom date:_____

Transplant / propagate / divide:_____

_____

_____

_____

Pests / problems:_____

_____

_____

_____

Notes:_____

_____

_____

_____

_____

_____

_____

_____

_____

Photo / plant tag / seed packet / drawing:

Common name:_____

Botanical name:_____

Purchased at:_____ Price:_____

☐ Annual   ☐ Perennial   ☐ Flower   ☐ Shrub   ☐ Tree

☐ Bareroot   ☐ Groundcover   ☐ Fruit   ☐ Vegetable ☐ Herb

Started from: ☐ Seed   ☐ Plant

Date germinated:_____ Date planted:_____

Location planted:_____

Planting instructions:_____

_____

_____

Sunlight: ☐ Full sun   ☐ Partial sun   ☐ Shade

Water requirements:_____ Size at maturity:_____

Care instructions:_____

_____

_____

_____

_____

Fertilizer / soil amendment / herbicide:_____

_____

_____

Harvest / bloom date:_____

Transplant / propagate / divide:_____

_____

_____

_____

Pests / problems:_____

_____

_____

_____

© 1998 Journals Unlimited, Inc., Bay City, MI The "Write It Down" ® Series

Notes:_____

_____

_____

_____

_____

_____

_____

_____

_____

Photo / plant tag / seed packet / drawing:

Common name:_____

Botanical name:_____

Purchased at:_____ Price:_____

☐ Annual   ☐ Perennial   ☐ Flower   ☐ Shrub   ☐ Tree

☐ Bareroot   ☐ Groundcover   ☐ Fruit   ☐ Vegetable   ☐ Herb

Started from: ☐ Seed   ☐ Plant

Date germinated:_____ Date planted:_____

Location planted:_____

Planting instructions:_____

_____

_____

Sunlight: ☐ Full sun   ☐ Partial sun   ☐ Shade

Water requirements:_____ Size at maturity:_____

Care instructions:_____

_____

_____

_____

_____

Fertilizer / soil amendment / herbicide:_____

_____

_____

Harvest / bloom date:_____

Transplant / propagate / divide:_____

_____

_____

_____

Pests / problems:_____

_____

_____

_____

Notes:_____

_____

_____

_____

_____

_____

_____

_____

Photo / plant tag / seed packet / drawing:

Common name:_____

Botanical name:_____

Purchased at:_____ Price:_____

☐ Annual ☐ Perennial ☐ Flower ☐ Shrub ☐ Tree

☐ Bareroot ☐ Groundcover ☐ Fruit ☐ Vegetable ☐ Herb

Started from: ☐ Seed ☐ Plant

Date germinated:_____ Date planted:_____

Location planted:_____

Planting instructions:_____

_____

_____

Sunlight: ☐ Full sun ☐ Partial sun ☐ Shade

Water requirements:_____ Size at maturity:_____

Care instructions:_____

_____

_____

_____

_____

Fertilizer / soil amendment / herbicide:_____

_____

_____

Harvest / bloom date:_____

Transplant / propagate / divide:_____

_____

_____

_____

Pests / problems:_____

_____

_____

_____

Notes:_____

_____

_____

_____

_____

_____

_____

_____

Photo / plant tag / seed packet / drawing:

Common name:_____

Botanical name:_____

Purchased at:_____ Price:_____

☐ Annual   ☐ Perennial   ☐ Flower   ☐ Shrub   ☐ Tree

☐ Bareroot   ☐ Groundcover   ☐ Fruit   ☐ Vegetable   ☐ Herb

Started from: ☐ Seed   ☐ Plant

Date germinated:_____ Date planted:_____

Location planted:_____

Planting instructions:_____

_____

_____

Sunlight: ☐ Full sun   ☐ Partial sun   ☐ Shade

Water requirements:_____ Size at maturity:_____

Care instructions:_____

_____

_____

_____

_____

Fertilizer / soil amendment / herbicide:_____

_____

_____

Harvest / bloom date:_____

Transplant / propagate / divide:_____

_____

_____

_____

Pests / problems:_____

_____

_____

_____

Notes:_____

_____

_____

_____

_____

_____

_____

_____

_____

Photo / plant tag / seed packet / drawing:

Common name:_____

Botanical name:_____

Purchased at:_____ Price:_____

☐ Annual   ☐ Perennial   ☐ Flower   ☐ Shrub   ☐ Tree

☐ Bareroot   ☐ Groundcover   ☐ Fruit   ☐ Vegetable   ☐ Herb

Started from: ☐ Seed   ☐ Plant

Date germinated:_____ Date planted:_____

Location planted:_____

Planting instructions:_____

_____

_____

Sunlight: ☐ Full sun   ☐ Partial sun   ☐ Shade

Water requirements:_____ Size at maturity:_____

Care instructions:_____

_____

_____

_____

_____

Fertilizer / soil amendment / herbicide:_____

_____

_____

Harvest / bloom date:_____

Transplant / propagate / divide:_____

_____

_____

_____

Pests / problems:_____

_____

_____

_____

Notes:_____

_____

_____

_____

_____

_____

_____

_____

Photo / plant tag / seed packet / drawing:

Common name:_____

Botanical name:_____

Purchased at:_____ Price:_____

☐ Annual ☐ Perennial ☐ Flower ☐ Shrub ☐ Tree

☐ Bareroot ☐ Groundcover ☐ Fruit ☐ Vegetable ☐ Herb

Started from: ☐ Seed ☐ Plant

Date germinated:_____ Date planted:_____

Location planted:_____

Planting instructions:_____

_____

_____

Sunlight: ☐ Full sun ☐ Partial sun ☐ Shade

Water requirements:_____ Size at maturity:_____

Care instructions:_____

_____

_____

_____

_____

Fertilizer / soil amendment / herbicide:_____

_____

_____

Harvest / bloom date:_____

Transplant / propagate / divide:_____

_____

_____

_____

Pests / problems:_____

_____

_____

_____

Notes:_____

_____

_____

_____

_____

_____

_____

_____

Photo / plant tag / seed packet / drawing:

Common name:_____

Botanical name:_____

Purchased at:_____ Price:_____

☐ Annual ☐ Perennial ☐ Flower ☐ Shrub ☐ Tree

☐ Bareroot ☐ Groundcover ☐ Fruit ☐ Vegetable ☐ Herb

Started from: ☐ Seed ☐ Plant

Date germinated:_____ Date planted:_____

Location planted:_____

Planting instructions:_____

_____

_____

Sunlight: ☐ Full sun ☐ Partial sun ☐ Shade

Water requirements:_____ Size at maturity:_____

Care instructions:_____

_____

_____

_____

_____

Fertilizer / soil amendment / herbicide:_____

_____

_____

Harvest / bloom date:_____

Transplant / propagate / divide:_____

_____

_____

_____

Pests / problems:_____

_____

_____

_____

Notes:_____

_____

_____

_____

_____

_____

_____

_____

Photo / plant tag / seed packet / drawing:

Common name:_____

Botanical name:_____

Purchased at:_____ Price:_____

☐ Annual   ☐ Perennial   ☐ Flower   ☐ Shrub   ☐ Tree

☐ Bareroot   ☐ Groundcover   ☐ Fruit   ☐ Vegetable   ☐ Herb

Started from: ☐ Seed   ☐ Plant

Date germinated:_____ Date planted:_____

Location planted:_____

Planting instructions:_____

_____

_____

Sunlight: ☐ Full sun   ☐ Partial sun   ☐ Shade

Water requirements:_____ Size at maturity:_____

Care instructions:_____

_____

_____

_____

_____

Fertilizer / soil amendment / herbicide:_____

_____

_____

Harvest / bloom date:_____

Transplant / propagate / divide:_____

_____

_____

_____

Pests / problems:_____

_____

_____

_____

Notes:_____

_____

_____

_____

_____

_____

_____

_____

Photo / plant tag / seed packet / drawing:

Common name:_____

Botanical name:_____

Purchased at:_____ Price:_____

☐ Annual   ☐ Perennial   ☐ Flower   ☐ Shrub   ☐ Tree

☐ Bareroot   ☐ Groundcover   ☐ Fruit   ☐ Vegetable   ☐ Herb

Started from: ☐ Seed   ☐ Plant

Date germinated:_____ Date planted:_____

Location planted:_____

Planting instructions:_____

_____

_____

Sunlight: ☐ Full sun   ☐ Partial sun   ☐ Shade

Water requirements:_____ Size at maturity:_____

Care instructions:_____

_____

_____

_____

_____

Fertilizer / soil amendment / herbicide:_____

_____

_____

Harvest / bloom date:_____

Transplant / propagate / divide:_____

_____

_____

_____

Pests / problems:_____

_____

_____

_____

Notes:_____

_____

_____

_____

_____

_____

_____

_____

_____

Photo / plant tag / seed packet / drawing:

Common name:_____

Botanical name:_____

Purchased at:_____ Price:_____

☐ Annual ☐ Perennial ☐ Flower ☐ Shrub ☐ Tree

☐ Bareroot ☐ Groundcover ☐ Fruit ☐ Vegetable ☐ Herb

Started from: ☐ Seed ☐ Plant

Date germinated:_____ Date planted:_____

Location planted:_____

Planting instructions:_____

_____

_____

Sunlight: ☐ Full sun ☐ Partial sun ☐ Shade

Water requirements:_____ Size at maturity:_____

Care instructions:_____

_____

_____

_____

Fertilizer / soil amendment / herbicide:_____

_____

_____

Harvest / bloom date:_____

Transplant / propagate / divide:_____

_____

_____

Pests / problems:_____

_____

_____

_____

Notes:_____

_____

_____

_____

_____

_____

_____

_____

Photo / plant tag / seed packet / drawing:

Common name:_____

Botanical name:_____

Purchased at:_____ Price:_____

☐ Annual   ☐ Perennial   ☐ Flower   ☐ Shrub   ☐ Tree

☐ Bareroot   ☐ Groundcover   ☐ Fruit   ☐ Vegetable   ☐ Herb

Started from: ☐ Seed   ☐ Plant

Date germinated:_____ Date planted:_____

Location planted:_____

Planting instructions:_____

_____

_____

Sunlight: ☐ Full sun   ☐ Partial sun   ☐ Shade

Water requirements:_____ Size at maturity:_____

Care instructions:_____

_____

_____

_____

Fertilizer / soil amendment / herbicide:_____

_____

_____

Harvest / bloom date:_____

Transplant / propagate / divide:_____

_____

_____

_____

Pests / problems:_____

_____

_____

_____

Notes:_____

_____

_____

_____

_____

_____

_____

_____

Photo / plant tag / seed packet / drawing:

Common name:_____

Botanical name:_____

Purchased at:_____ Price:_____

☐ Annual   ☐ Perennial   ☐ Flower   ☐ Shrub   ☐ Tree

☐ Bareroot   ☐ Groundcover   ☐ Fruit   ☐ Vegetable   ☐ Herb

Started from: ☐ Seed   ☐ Plant

Date germinated:_____ Date planted:_____

Location planted:_____

Planting instructions:_____

_____

_____

Sunlight: ☐ Full sun   ☐ Partial sun   ☐ Shade

Water requirements:_____ Size at maturity:_____

Care instructions:_____

_____

_____

_____

_____

Fertilizer / soil amendment / herbicide:_____

_____

_____

Harvest / bloom date:_____

Transplant / propagate / divide:_____

_____

_____

_____

Pests / problems:_____

_____

_____

_____

Notes:_____

_____

_____

_____

_____

_____

_____

_____

Photo / plant tag / seed packet / drawing:

Common name:_____

Botanical name:_____

Purchased at:_____ Price:_____

☐ Annual ☐ Perennial ☐ Flower ☐ Shrub ☐ Tree

☐ Bareroot ☐ Groundcover ☐ Fruit ☐ Vegetable ☐ Herb

Started from: ☐ Seed ☐ Plant

Date germinated:_____ Date planted:_____

Location planted:_____

Planting instructions:_____

_____

_____

Sunlight: ☐ Full sun ☐ Partial sun ☐ Shade

Water requirements:_____ Size at maturity:_____

Care instructions:_____

_____

_____

_____

_____

Fertilizer / soil amendment / herbicide:_____

_____

_____

Harvest / bloom date:_____

Transplant / propagate / divide:_____

_____

_____

_____

Pests / problems:_____

_____

_____

_____

Notes:_____

_____

_____

_____

_____

_____

_____

_____

_____

Photo / plant tag / seed packet / drawing:

Common name:_____

Botanical name:_____

Purchased at:_____ Price:_____

☐ Annual   ☐ Perennial   ☐ Flower   ☐ Shrub   ☐ Tree

☐ Bareroot   ☐ Groundcover   ☐ Fruit   ☐ Vegetable   ☐ Herb

Started from: ☐ Seed   ☐ Plant

Date germinated:_____ Date planted:_____

Location planted:_____

Planting instructions:_____

_____

_____

Sunlight: ☐ Full sun   ☐ Partial sun   ☐ Shade

Water requirements:_____ Size at maturity:_____

Care instructions:_____

_____

_____

_____

_____

Fertilizer / soil amendment / herbicide:_____

_____

_____

Harvest / bloom date:_____

Transplant / propagate / divide:_____

_____

_____

Pests / problems:_____

_____

_____

_____

Notes:_____

_____

_____

_____

_____

_____

_____

_____

Photo / plant tag / seed packet / drawing:

Common name:_____

Botanical name:_____

Purchased at:_____ Price:_____

☐ Annual   ☐ Perennial   ☐ Flower   ☐ Shrub   ☐ Tree

☐ Bareroot   ☐ Groundcover   ☐ Fruit   ☐ Vegetable   ☐ Herb

Started from: ☐ Seed   ☐ Plant

Date germinated:_____ Date planted:_____

Location planted:_____

Planting instructions:_____

_____

_____

Sunlight: ☐ Full sun   ☐ Partial sun   ☐ Shade

Water requirements:_____ Size at maturity:_____

Care instructions:_____

_____

_____

_____

_____

Fertilizer / soil amendment / herbicide:_____

_____

_____

Harvest / bloom date:_____

Transplant / propagate / divide:_____

_____

_____

_____

Pests / problems:_____

_____

_____

_____

Notes:_____

_____

_____

_____

_____

_____

_____

_____

Photo / plant tag / seed packet / drawing:

Common name:_____

Botanical name:_____

Purchased at:_____ Price:_____

☐ Annual ☐ Perennial ☐ Flower ☐ Shrub ☐ Tree

☐ Bareroot ☐ Groundcover ☐ Fruit ☐ Vegetable ☐ Herb

Started from: ☐ Seed ☐ Plant

Date germinated:_____ Date planted:_____

Location planted:_____

Planting instructions:_____

_____

_____

Sunlight: ☐ Full sun ☐ Partial sun ☐ Shade

Water requirements:_____ Size at maturity:_____

Care instructions:_____

_____

_____

_____

Fertilizer / soil amendment / herbicide:_____

_____

_____

Harvest / bloom date:_____

Transplant / propagate / divide:_____

_____

_____

_____

Pests / problems:_____

_____

_____

_____

Notes:_____

_____

_____

_____

_____

_____

_____

_____

Photo / plant tag / seed packet / drawing:

Common name:_____

Botanical name:_____

Purchased at:_____ Price:_____

☐ Annual ☐ Perennial ☐ Flower ☐ Shrub ☐ Tree

☐ Bareroot ☐ Groundcover ☐ Fruit ☐ Vegetable ☐ Herb

Started from: ☐ Seed ☐ Plant

Date germinated:_____ Date planted:_____

Location planted:_____

Planting instructions:_____

_____

_____

Sunlight: ☐ Full sun ☐ Partial sun ☐ Shade

Water requirements:_____ Size at maturity:_____

Care instructions:_____

_____

_____

_____

Fertilizer / soil amendment / herbicide:_____

_____

_____

Harvest / bloom date:_____

Transplant / propagate / divide:_____

_____

_____

_____

Pests / problems:_____

_____

_____

_____

Notes:_____

_____

_____

_____

_____

_____

_____

_____

_____

Photo / plant tag / seed packet / drawing:

Common name:_____

Botanical name:_____

Purchased at:_____ Price:_____

☐ Annual   ☐ Perennial   ☐ Flower   ☐ Shrub   ☐ Tree

☐ Bareroot   ☐ Groundcover   ☐ Fruit   ☐ Vegetable ☐ Herb

Started from: ☐ Seed   ☐ Plant

Date germinated:_____ Date planted:_____

Location planted:_____

Planting instructions:_____

_____

_____

Sunlight: ☐ Full sun   ☐ Partial sun   ☐ Shade

Water requirements:_____ Size at maturity:_____

Care instructions:_____

_____

_____

_____

_____

Fertilizer / soil amendment / herbicide:_____

_____

_____

Harvest / bloom date:_____

Transplant / propagate / divide:_____

_____

_____

_____

Pests / problems:_____

_____

_____

_____

Notes:_____

_____

_____

_____

_____

_____

_____

_____

Photo / plant tag / seed packet / drawing:

Common name:_____

Botanical name:_____

Purchased at:_____ Price:_____

☐ Annual   ☐ Perennial   ☐ Flower   ☐ Shrub   ☐ Tree

☐ Bareroot   ☐ Groundcover   ☐ Fruit   ☐ Vegetable   ☐ Herb

Started from: ☐ Seed   ☐ Plant

Date germinated:_____ Date planted:_____

Location planted:_____

Planting instructions:_____

_____

_____

Sunlight: ☐ Full sun   ☐ Partial sun   ☐ Shade

Water requirements:_____ Size at maturity:_____

Care instructions:_____

_____

_____

_____

Fertilizer / soil amendment / herbicide:_____

_____

_____

Harvest / bloom date:_____

Transplant / propagate / divide:_____

_____

_____

Pests / problems:_____

_____

_____

_____

Notes:_____

_____

_____

_____

_____

_____

_____

_____

Photo / plant tag / seed packet / drawing:

Common name:_____

Botanical name:_____

Purchased at:_____ Price:_____

☐ Annual   ☐ Perennial   ☐ Flower   ☐ Shrub   ☐ Tree

☐ Bareroot   ☐ Groundcover   ☐ Fruit   ☐ Vegetable   ☐ Herb

Started from: ☐ Seed   ☐ Plant

Date germinated:_____ Date planted:_____

Location planted:_____

Planting instructions:_____

_____

_____

Sunlight: ☐ Full sun   ☐ Partial sun   ☐ Shade

Water requirements:_____ Size at maturity:_____

Care instructions:_____

_____

_____

_____

_____

Fertilizer / soil amendment / herbicide:_____

_____

_____

Harvest / bloom date:_____

Transplant / propagate / divide:_____

_____

_____

_____

Pests / problems:_____

_____

_____

_____

Notes:_____

_____

_____

_____

_____

_____

_____

_____

Photo / plant tag / seed packet / drawing:

Common name:_____

Botanical name:_____

Purchased at:_____ Price:_____

☐ Annual   ☐ Perennial   ☐ Flower   ☐ Shrub   ☐ Tree

☐ Bareroot   ☐ Groundcover   ☐ Fruit   ☐ Vegetable   ☐ Herb

Started from: ☐ Seed   ☐ Plant

Date germinated:_____ Date planted:_____

Location planted:_____

Planting instructions:_____

_____

_____

Sunlight: ☐ Full sun   ☐ Partial sun   ☐ Shade

Water requirements:_____ Size at maturity:_____

Care instructions:_____

_____

_____

_____

_____

Fertilizer / soil amendment / herbicide:_____

_____

_____

Harvest / bloom date:_____

Transplant / propagate / divide:_____

_____

_____

_____

Pests / problems:_____

_____

_____

_____

Notes:_____

_____

_____

_____

_____

_____

_____

_____

_____

Photo / plant tag / seed packet / drawing:

Common name:_____

Botanical name:_____

Purchased at:_____ Price:_____

☐ Annual ☐ Perennial ☐ Flower ☐ Shrub ☐ Tree

☐ Bareroot ☐ Groundcover ☐ Fruit ☐ Vegetable ☐ Herb

Started from: ☐ Seed ☐ Plant

Date germinated:_____ Date planted:_____

Location planted:_____

Planting instructions:_____

_____

_____

Sunlight: ☐ Full sun ☐ Partial sun ☐ Shade

Water requirements:_____ Size at maturity:_____

Care instructions:_____

_____

_____

_____

_____

Fertilizer / soil amendment / herbicide:_____

_____

_____

Harvest / bloom date:_____

Transplant / propagate / divide:_____

_____

_____

_____

Pests / problems:_____

_____

_____

_____

Notes:_____

_____

_____

_____

_____

_____

_____

_____

Photo / plant tag / seed packet / drawing:

Common name:_____

Botanical name:_____

Purchased at:_____ Price:_____

☐ Annual ☐ Perennial ☐ Flower ☐ Shrub ☐ Tree

☐ Bareroot ☐ Groundcover ☐ Fruit ☐ Vegetable ☐ Herb

Started from: ☐ Seed ☐ Plant

Date germinated:_____ Date planted:_____

Location planted:_____

Planting instructions:_____

_____

_____

Sunlight: ☐ Full sun ☐ Partial sun ☐ Shade

Water requirements:_____ Size at maturity:_____

Care instructions:_____

_____

_____

_____

Fertilizer / soil amendment / herbicide:_____

_____

_____

Harvest / bloom date:_____

Transplant / propagate / divide:_____

_____

_____

_____

Pests / problems:_____

_____

_____

_____

Notes:_____

_____

_____

_____

_____

_____

_____

_____

_____

Photo / plant tag / seed packet / drawing:

Common name:_____

Botanical name:_____

Purchased at:_____ Price:_____

☐ Annual   ☐ Perennial   ☐ Flower   ☐ Shrub   ☐ Tree

☐ Bareroot   ☐ Groundcover   ☐ Fruit   ☐ Vegetable   ☐ Herb

Started from: ☐ Seed   ☐ Plant

Date germinated:_____ Date planted:_____

Location planted:_____

Planting instructions:_____

_____

_____

Sunlight: ☐ Full sun   ☐ Partial sun   ☐ Shade

Water requirements:_____ Size at maturity:_____

Care instructions:_____

_____

_____

_____

_____

Fertilizer / soil amendment / herbicide:_____

_____

_____

Harvest / bloom date:_____

Transplant / propagate / divide:_____

_____

_____

_____

Pests / problems:_____

_____

_____

_____

Notes:_____

_____

_____

_____

_____

_____

_____

_____

Photo / plant tag / seed packet / drawing:

Common name:_____

Botanical name:_____

Purchased at:_____ Price:_____

☐ Annual   ☐ Perennial   ☐ Flower   ☐ Shrub   ☐ Tree

☐ Bareroot   ☐ Groundcover   ☐ Fruit   ☐ Vegetable   ☐ Herb

Started from: ☐ Seed   ☐ Plant

Date germinated:_____ Date planted:_____

Location planted:_____

Planting instructions:_____

_____

_____

Sunlight: ☐ Full sun   ☐ Partial sun   ☐ Shade

Water requirements:_____ Size at maturity:_____

Care instructions:_____

_____

_____

_____

_____

Fertilizer / soil amendment / herbicide:_____

_____

_____

Harvest / bloom date:_____

Transplant / propagate / divide:_____

_____

_____

_____

Pests / problems:_____

_____

_____

_____

Notes:_____

_____

_____

_____

_____

_____

_____

_____

Photo / plant tag / seed packet / drawing:

Common name:_____

Botanical name:_____

Purchased at:_____ Price:_____

☐ Annual   ☐ Perennial   ☐ Flower   ☐ Shrub   ☐ Tree

☐ Bareroot   ☐ Groundcover   ☐ Fruit   ☐ Vegetable   ☐ Herb

Started from: ☐ Seed   ☐ Plant

Date germinated:_____ Date planted:_____

Location planted:_____

Planting instructions:_____

_____

_____

Sunlight: ☐ Full sun   ☐ Partial sun   ☐ Shade

Water requirements:_____ Size at maturity:_____

Care instructions:_____

_____

_____

_____

_____

Fertilizer / soil amendment / herbicide:_____

_____

_____

Harvest / bloom date:_____

Transplant / propagate / divide:_____

_____

_____

_____

Pests / problems:_____

_____

_____

_____

Notes:_____

_____

_____

_____

_____

_____

_____

_____

Photo / plant tag / seed packet / drawing:

Common name:_____

Botanical name:_____

Purchased at:_____ Price:_____

☐ Annual ☐ Perennial ☐ Flower ☐ Shrub ☐ Tree

☐ Bareroot ☐ Groundcover ☐ Fruit ☐ Vegetable ☐ Herb

Started from: ☐ Seed ☐ Plant

Date germinated:_____ Date planted:_____

Location planted:_____

Planting instructions:_____

_____

_____

Sunlight: ☐ Full sun ☐ Partial sun ☐ Shade

Water requirements:_____ Size at maturity:_____

Care instructions:_____

_____

_____

_____

_____

Fertilizer / soil amendment / herbicide:_____

_____

_____

Harvest / bloom date:_____

Transplant / propagate / divide:_____

_____

_____

Pests / problems:_____

_____

_____

_____

Notes:_____

_____

_____

_____

_____

_____

_____

_____

_____

Photo / plant tag / seed packet / drawing:

Common name:_____

Botanical name:_____

Purchased at:_____ Price:_____

☐ Annual   ☐ Perennial   ☐ Flower   ☐ Shrub   ☐ Tree

☐ Bareroot   ☐ Groundcover   ☐ Fruit   ☐ Vegetable   ☐ Herb

Started from: ☐ Seed   ☐ Plant

Date germinated:_____ Date planted:_____

Location planted:_____

Planting instructions:_____

_____

_____

Sunlight: ☐ Full sun   ☐ Partial sun   ☐ Shade

Water requirements:_____ Size at maturity:_____

Care instructions:_____

_____

_____

_____

_____

Fertilizer / soil amendment / herbicide:_____

_____

_____

Harvest / bloom date:_____

Transplant / propagate / divide:_____

_____

_____

_____

Pests / problems:_____

_____

_____

_____

Notes:_____

_____

_____

_____

_____

_____

_____

_____

Photo / plant tag / seed packet / drawing:

Common name:_____

Botanical name:_____

Purchased at:_____ Price:_____

☐ Annual ☐ Perennial ☐ Flower ☐ Shrub ☐ Tree

☐ Bareroot ☐ Groundcover ☐ Fruit ☐ Vegetable ☐ Herb

Started from: ☐ Seed ☐ Plant

Date germinated:_____ Date planted:_____

Location planted:_____

Planting instructions:_____

_____

_____

Sunlight: ☐ Full sun ☐ Partial sun ☐ Shade

Water requirements:_____ Size at maturity:_____

Care instructions:_____

_____

_____

_____

_____

Fertilizer / soil amendment / herbicide:_____

_____

_____

Harvest / bloom date:_____

Transplant / propagate / divide:_____

_____

_____

_____

Pests / problems:_____

_____

_____

_____

Notes:_____

_____

_____

_____

_____

_____

_____

_____

_____

Photo / plant tag / seed packet / drawing:

Common name:_____

Botanical name:_____

Purchased at:_____ Price:_____

☐ Annual ☐ Perennial ☐ Flower ☐ Shrub ☐ Tree

☐ Bareroot ☐ Groundcover ☐ Fruit ☐ Vegetable ☐ Herb

Started from: ☐ Seed ☐ Plant

Date germinated:_____ Date planted:_____

Location planted:_____

Planting instructions:_____

_____

_____

Sunlight: ☐ Full sun ☐ Partial sun ☐ Shade

Water requirements:_____ Size at maturity:_____

Care instructions:_____

_____

_____

_____

Fertilizer / soil amendment / herbicide:_____

_____

_____

Harvest / bloom date:_____

Transplant / propagate / divide:_____

_____

_____

Pests / problems:_____

_____

_____

_____

Notes:_____

_____

_____

_____

_____

_____

_____

_____

_____

Photo / plant tag / seed packet / drawing:

Common name:_____

Botanical name:_____

Purchased at:_____ Price:_____

☐ Annual   ☐ Perennial   ☐ Flower   ☐ Shrub   ☐ Tree

☐ Bareroot   ☐ Groundcover   ☐ Fruit   ☐ Vegetable   ☐ Herb

Started from: ☐ Seed   ☐ Plant

Date germinated:_____ Date planted:_____

Location planted:_____

Planting instructions:_____

_____

_____

Sunlight: ☐ Full sun   ☐ Partial sun   ☐ Shade

Water requirements:_____ Size at maturity:_____

Care instructions:_____

_____

_____

_____

_____

Fertilizer / soil amendment / herbicide:_____

_____

_____

Harvest / bloom date:_____

Transplant / propagate / divide:_____

_____

_____

_____

Pests / problems:_____

_____

_____

_____

Notes:_____

_____

_____

_____

_____

_____

_____

_____

Photo / plant tag / seed packet / drawing:

Common name:_____

Botanical name:_____

Purchased at:_____ Price:_____

☐ Annual   ☐ Perennial   ☐ Flower   ☐ Shrub   ☐ Tree

☐ Bareroot   ☐ Groundcover   ☐ Fruit   ☐ Vegetable   ☐ Herb

Started from: ☐ Seed   ☐ Plant

Date germinated:_____ Date planted:_____

Location planted:_____

Planting instructions:_____

_____

_____

Sunlight: ☐ Full sun   ☐ Partial sun   ☐ Shade

Water requirements:_____ Size at maturity:_____

Care instructions:_____

_____

_____

_____

_____

Fertilizer / soil amendment / herbicide:_____

_____

_____

_____

Harvest / bloom date:_____

Transplant / propagate / divide:_____

_____

_____

_____

Pests / problems:_____

_____

_____

_____

Notes:_____

_____

_____

_____

_____

_____

_____

_____

Photo / plant tag / seed packet / drawing:

Common name:_____

Botanical name:_____

Purchased at:_____ Price:_____

☐ Annual   ☐ Perennial   ☐ Flower   ☐ Shrub   ☐ Tree

☐ Bareroot   ☐ Groundcover   ☐ Fruit   ☐ Vegetable   ☐ Herb

Started from: ☐ Seed   ☐ Plant

Date germinated:_____ Date planted:_____

Location planted:_____

Planting instructions:_____

_____

_____

Sunlight: ☐ Full sun   ☐ Partial sun   ☐ Shade

Water requirements:_____ Size at maturity:_____

Care instructions:_____

_____

_____

_____

_____

Fertilizer / soil amendment / herbicide:_____

_____

_____

Harvest / bloom date:_____

Transplant / propagate / divide:_____

_____

_____

_____

Pests / problems:_____

_____

_____

_____

Notes:_____

_____

_____

_____

_____

_____

_____

_____

Photo / plant tag / seed packet / drawing:

Common name:_____

Botanical name:_____

Purchased at:_____ Price:_____

☐ Annual　　☐ Perennial　　☐ Flower　　☐ Shrub　　☐ Tree

☐ Bareroot　☐ Groundcover　☐ Fruit　　☐ Vegetable　☐ Herb

Started from: ☐ Seed　☐ Plant

Date germinated:_____ Date planted:_____

Location planted:_____

Planting instructions:_____

_____

_____

Sunlight: ☐ Full sun　☐ Partial sun　☐ Shade

Water requirements:_____ Size at maturity:_____

Care instructions:_____

_____

_____

_____

_____

Fertilizer / soil amendment / herbicide:_____

_____

_____

Harvest / bloom date:_____

Transplant / propagate / divide:_____

_____

_____

_____

Pests / problems:_____

_____

_____

_____

Notes:_____

_____

_____

_____

_____

_____

_____

_____

Photo / plant tag / seed packet / drawing:

Common name:_____

Botanical name:_____

Purchased at:_____ Price:_____

☐ Annual ☐ Perennial ☐ Flower ☐ Shrub ☐ Tree

☐ Bareroot ☐ Groundcover ☐ Fruit ☐ Vegetable ☐ Herb

Started from: ☐ Seed ☐ Plant

Date germinated:_____ Date planted:_____

Location planted:_____

Planting instructions:_____

_____

_____

Sunlight: ☐ Full sun ☐ Partial sun ☐ Shade

Water requirements:_____ Size at maturity:_____

Care instructions:_____

_____

_____

_____

_____

Fertilizer / soil amendment / herbicide:_____

_____

_____

Harvest / bloom date:_____

Transplant / propagate / divide:_____

_____

_____

_____

Pests / problems:_____

_____

_____

_____

Notes:_____

_____

_____

_____

_____

_____

_____

_____

Photo / plant tag / seed packet / drawing:

Common name:_____

Botanical name:_____

Purchased at:_____ Price:_____

☐ Annual ☐ Perennial ☐ Flower ☐ Shrub ☐ Tree

☐ Bareroot ☐ Groundcover ☐ Fruit ☐ Vegetable ☐ Herb

Started from: ☐ Seed ☐ Plant

Date germinated:_____ Date planted:_____

Location planted:_____

Planting instructions:_____

_____

_____

Sunlight: ☐ Full sun ☐ Partial sun ☐ Shade

Water requirements:_____ Size at maturity:_____

Care instructions:_____

_____

_____

_____

_____

Fertilizer / soil amendment / herbicide:_____

_____

_____

Harvest / bloom date:_____

Transplant / propagate / divide:_____

_____

_____

_____

Pests / problems:_____

_____

_____

_____

Notes:_____

_____

_____

_____

_____

_____

_____

_____

Photo / plant tag / seed packet / drawing:

Common name:_____

Botanical name:_____

Purchased at:_____ Price:_____

☐ Annual   ☐ Perennial   ☐ Flower   ☐ Shrub   ☐ Tree

☐ Bareroot   ☐ Groundcover   ☐ Fruit   ☐ Vegetable   ☐ Herb

Started from: ☐ Seed   ☐ Plant

Date germinated:_____ Date planted:_____

Location planted:_____

Planting instructions:_____

_____

_____

Sunlight: ☐ Full sun   ☐ Partial sun   ☐ Shade

Water requirements:_____ Size at maturity:_____

Care instructions:_____

_____

_____

_____

Fertilizer / soil amendment / herbicide:_____

_____

_____

Harvest / bloom date:_____

Transplant / propagate / divide:_____

_____

_____

Pests / problems:_____

_____

_____

_____

Notes:_____

_____

_____

_____

_____

_____

_____

_____

Photo / plant tag / seed packet / drawing:

Common name:_____

Botanical name:_____

Purchased at:_____ Price:_____

☐ Annual   ☐ Perennial   ☐ Flower   ☐ Shrub   ☐ Tree

☐ Bareroot   ☐ Groundcover   ☐ Fruit   ☐ Vegetable   ☐ Herb

Started from: ☐ Seed   ☐ Plant

Date germinated:_____ Date planted:_____

Location planted:_____

Planting instructions:_____

_____

_____

Sunlight: ☐ Full sun   ☐ Partial sun   ☐ Shade

Water requirements:_____ Size at maturity:_____

Care instructions:_____

_____

_____

_____

Fertilizer / soil amendment / herbicide:_____

_____

_____

Harvest / bloom date:_____

Transplant / propagate / divide:_____

_____

_____

_____

Pests / problems:_____

_____

_____

_____

Notes:_____

_____

_____

_____

_____

_____

_____

_____

Photo / plant tag / seed packet / drawing:

Common name:_____

Botanical name:_____

Purchased at:_____ Price:_____

☐ Annual   ☐ Perennial   ☐ Flower   ☐ Shrub   ☐ Tree

☐ Bareroot   ☐ Groundcover   ☐ Fruit   ☐ Vegetable   ☐ Herb

Started from: ☐ Seed   ☐ Plant

Date germinated:_____ Date planted:_____

Location planted:_____

Planting instructions:_____

_____

_____

Sunlight: ☐ Full sun   ☐ Partial sun   ☐ Shade

Water requirements:_____ Size at maturity:_____

Care instructions:_____

_____

_____

_____

_____

Fertilizer / soil amendment / herbicide:_____

_____

_____

Harvest / bloom date:_____

Transplant / propagate / divide:_____

_____

_____

_____

Pests / problems:_____

_____

_____

_____

Notes:_____

_____

_____

_____

_____

_____

_____

_____

_____

Photo / plant tag / seed packet / drawing:

Common name:_____

Botanical name:_____

Purchased at:_____ Price:_____

☐ Annual ☐ Perennial ☐ Flower ☐ Shrub ☐ Tree

☐ Bareroot ☐ Groundcover ☐ Fruit ☐ Vegetable ☐ Herb

Started from: ☐ Seed ☐ Plant

Date germinated:_____ Date planted:_____

Location planted:_____

Planting instructions:_____

_____

_____

Sunlight: ☐ Full sun ☐ Partial sun ☐ Shade

Water requirements:_____ Size at maturity:_____

Care instructions:_____

_____

_____

_____

_____

Fertilizer / soil amendment / herbicide:_____

_____

_____

Harvest / bloom date:_____

Transplant / propagate / divide:_____

_____

_____

Pests / problems:_____

_____

_____

_____

Notes:_____

_____

_____

_____

_____

_____

_____

_____

Photo / plant tag / seed packet / drawing:

Common name:_____

Botanical name:_____

Purchased at:_____ Price:_____

☐ Annual ☐ Perennial ☐ Flower ☐ Shrub ☐ Tree

☐ Bareroot ☐ Groundcover ☐ Fruit ☐ Vegetable ☐ Herb

Started from: ☐ Seed ☐ Plant

Date germinated:_____ Date planted:_____

Location planted:_____

Planting instructions:_____

_____

_____

Sunlight: ☐ Full sun ☐ Partial sun ☐ Shade

Water requirements:_____ Size at maturity:_____

Care instructions:_____

_____

_____

_____

_____

Fertilizer / soil amendment / herbicide:_____

_____

_____

Harvest / bloom date:_____

Transplant / propagate / divide:_____

_____

_____

_____

Pests / problems:_____

_____

_____

_____

Notes:_____

_____

_____

_____

_____

_____

_____

_____

Photo / plant tag / seed packet / drawing:

Common name:_____

Botanical name:_____

Purchased at:_____ Price:_____

☐ Annual ☐ Perennial ☐ Flower ☐ Shrub ☐ Tree

☐ Bareroot ☐ Groundcover ☐ Fruit ☐ Vegetable ☐ Herb

Started from: ☐ Seed ☐ Plant

Date germinated:_____ Date planted:_____

Location planted:_____

Planting instructions:_____

_____

_____

Sunlight: ☐ Full sun ☐ Partial sun ☐ Shade

Water requirements:_____ Size at maturity:_____

Care instructions:_____

_____

_____

_____

_____

Fertilizer / soil amendment / herbicide:_____

_____

_____

Harvest / bloom date:_____

Transplant / propagate / divide:_____

_____

_____

_____

Pests / problems:_____

_____

_____

_____

Notes:

Photo / plant tag / seed packet / drawing:

Common name:_____

Botanical name:_____

Purchased at:_____ Price:_____

☐ Annual ☐ Perennial ☐ Flower ☐ Shrub ☐ Tree

☐ Bareroot ☐ Groundcover ☐ Fruit ☐ Vegetable ☐ Herb

Started from: ☐ Seed ☐ Plant

Date germinated:_____ Date planted:_____

Location planted:_____

Planting instructions:_____

_____

_____

Sunlight: ☐ Full sun ☐ Partial sun ☐ Shade

Water requirements:_____ Size at maturity:_____

Care instructions:_____

_____

_____

_____

_____

Fertilizer / soil amendment / herbicide:_____

_____

_____

Harvest / bloom date:_____

Transplant / propagate / divide:_____

_____

_____

_____

Pests / problems:_____

_____

_____

_____

Notes:_____

_____

_____

_____

_____

_____

_____

_____

Photo / plant tag / seed packet / drawing:

Common name:_____

Botanical name:_____

Purchased at:_____ Price:_____

☐ Annual ☐ Perennial ☐ Flower ☐ Shrub ☐ Tree

☐ Bareroot ☐ Groundcover ☐ Fruit ☐ Vegetable ☐ Herb

Started from: ☐ Seed ☐ Plant

Date germinated:_____ Date planted:_____

Location planted:_____

Planting instructions:_____

_____

_____

Sunlight: ☐ Full sun ☐ Partial sun ☐ Shade

Water requirements:_____ Size at maturity:_____

Care instructions:_____

_____

_____

_____

_____

Fertilizer / soil amendment / herbicide:_____

_____

_____

Harvest / bloom date:_____

Transplant / propagate / divide:_____

_____

_____

_____

Pests / problems:_____

_____

_____

_____

Notes:_____

_____

_____

_____

_____

_____

_____

_____

_____

Photo / plant tag / seed packet / drawing:

Common name:_____

Botanical name:_____

Purchased at:_____ Price:_____

☐ Annual   ☐ Perennial   ☐ Flower   ☐ Shrub   ☐ Tree

☐ Bareroot   ☐ Groundcover   ☐ Fruit   ☐ Vegetable   ☐ Herb

Started from: ☐ Seed   ☐ Plant

Date germinated:_____ Date planted:_____

Location planted:_____

Planting instructions:_____

_____

_____

Sunlight: ☐ Full sun   ☐ Partial sun   ☐ Shade

Water requirements:_____ Size at maturity:_____

Care instructions:_____

_____

_____

_____

_____

Fertilizer / soil amendment / herbicide:_____

_____

_____

Harvest / bloom date:_____

Transplant / propagate / divide:_____

_____

_____

_____

Pests / problems:_____

_____

_____

_____

Notes:_____

_____

_____

_____

_____

_____

_____

_____

Photo / plant tag / seed packet / drawing:

Common name:_____

Botanical name:_____

Purchased at:_____ Price:_____

☐ Annual   ☐ Perennial   ☐ Flower   ☐ Shrub   ☐ Tree

☐ Bareroot   ☐ Groundcover   ☐ Fruit   ☐ Vegetable   ☐ Herb

Started from: ☐ Seed   ☐ Plant

Date germinated:_____ Date planted:_____

Location planted:_____

Planting instructions:_____

_____

_____

Sunlight: ☐ Full sun   ☐ Partial sun   ☐ Shade

Water requirements:_____ Size at maturity:_____

Care instructions:_____

_____

_____

_____

_____

Fertilizer / soil amendment / herbicide:_____

_____

_____

Harvest / bloom date:_____

Transplant / propagate / divide:_____

_____

_____

_____

Pests / problems:_____

_____

_____

_____

Notes:_____

_____

_____

_____

_____

_____

_____

_____

Photo / plant tag / seed packet / drawing:

Common name:_____

Botanical name:_____

Purchased at:_____ Price:_____

☐ Annual ☐ Perennial ☐ Flower ☐ Shrub ☐ Tree

☐ Bareroot ☐ Groundcover ☐ Fruit ☐ Vegetable ☐ Herb

Started from: ☐ Seed ☐ Plant

Date germinated:_____ Date planted:_____

Location planted:_____

Planting instructions:_____

_____

_____

Sunlight: ☐ Full sun ☐ Partial sun ☐ Shade

Water requirements:_____ Size at maturity:_____

Care instructions:_____

_____

_____

_____

_____

Fertilizer / soil amendment / herbicide:_____

_____

_____

Harvest / bloom date:_____

Transplant / propagate / divide:_____

_____

_____

Pests / problems:_____

_____

_____

_____

Notes:_____

_____

_____

_____

_____

_____

_____

_____

Photo / plant tag / seed packet / drawing:

Common name:_____

Botanical name:_____

Purchased at:_____ Price:_____

☐ Annual   ☐ Perennial   ☐ Flower   ☐ Shrub   ☐ Tree

☐ Bareroot   ☐ Groundcover   ☐ Fruit   ☐ Vegetable   ☐ Herb

Started from: ☐ Seed   ☐ Plant

Date germinated:_____ Date planted:_____

Location planted:_____

Planting instructions:_____

_____

_____

Sunlight: ☐ Full sun   ☐ Partial sun   ☐ Shade

Water requirements:_____ Size at maturity:_____

Care instructions:_____

_____

_____

_____

_____

Fertilizer / soil amendment / herbicide:_____

_____

_____

Harvest / bloom date:_____

Transplant / propagate / divide:_____

_____

_____

_____

Pests / problems:_____

_____

_____

_____

Notes:_____

_____

_____

_____

_____

_____

_____

_____

Photo / plant tag / seed packet / drawing:

Common name:_____

Botanical name:_____

Purchased at:_____ Price:_____

☐ Annual   ☐ Perennial   ☐ Flower   ☐ Shrub   ☐ Tree

☐ Bareroot   ☐ Groundcover   ☐ Fruit   ☐ Vegetable   ☐ Herb

Started from: ☐ Seed   ☐ Plant

Date germinated:_____ Date planted:_____

Location planted:_____

Planting instructions:_____

_____

_____

Sunlight: ☐ Full sun   ☐ Partial sun   ☐ Shade

Water requirements:_____ Size at maturity:_____

Care instructions:_____

_____

_____

_____

_____

Fertilizer / soil amendment / herbicide:_____

_____

_____

Harvest / bloom date:_____

Transplant / propagate / divide:_____

_____

_____

_____

Pests / problems:_____

_____

_____

_____

Notes:_____

_____

_____

_____

_____

_____

_____

_____

_____

Photo / plant tag / seed packet / drawing:

Common name:_____

Botanical name:_____

Purchased at:_____ Price:_____

☐ Annual ☐ Perennial ☐ Flower ☐ Shrub ☐ Tree

☐ Bareroot ☐ Groundcover ☐ Fruit ☐ Vegetable ☐ Herb

Started from: ☐ Seed ☐ Plant

Date germinated:_____ Date planted:_____

Location planted:_____

Planting instructions:_____

_____

_____

Sunlight: ☐ Full sun ☐ Partial sun ☐ Shade

Water requirements:_____ Size at maturity:_____

Care instructions:_____

_____

_____

_____

_____

Fertilizer / soil amendment / herbicide:_____

_____

_____

Harvest / bloom date:_____

Transplant / propagate / divide:_____

_____

_____

Pests / problems:_____

_____

_____

_____

Notes:_____

_____

_____

_____

_____

_____

_____

_____

_____

Photo / plant tag / seed packet / drawing:

Common name:_____

Botanical name:_____

Purchased at:_____ Price:_____

☐ Annual ☐ Perennial ☐ Flower ☐ Shrub ☐ Tree

☐ Bareroot ☐ Groundcover ☐ Fruit ☐ Vegetable ☐ Herb

Started from: ☐ Seed ☐ Plant

Date germinated:_____ Date planted:_____

Location planted:_____

Planting instructions:_____

_____

_____

Sunlight: ☐ Full sun ☐ Partial sun ☐ Shade

Water requirements:_____ Size at maturity:_____

Care instructions:_____

_____

_____

_____

_____

Fertilizer / soil amendment / herbicide:_____

_____

_____

Harvest / bloom date:_____

Transplant / propagate / divide:_____

_____

_____

_____

Pests / problems:_____

_____

_____

_____

Notes:_____

_____

_____

_____

_____

_____

_____

_____

Photo / plant tag / seed packet / drawing:

Common name:_____

Botanical name:_____

Purchased at:_____ Price:_____

☐ Annual ☐ Perennial ☐ Flower ☐ Shrub ☐ Tree

☐ Bareroot ☐ Groundcover ☐ Fruit ☐ Vegetable ☐ Herb

Started from: ☐ Seed ☐ Plant

Date germinated:_____ Date planted:_____

Location planted:_____

Planting instructions:_____

_____

_____

Sunlight: ☐ Full sun ☐ Partial sun ☐ Shade

Water requirements:_____ Size at maturity:_____

Care instructions:_____

_____

_____

_____

_____

Fertilizer / soil amendment / herbicide:_____

_____

_____

Harvest / bloom date:_____

Transplant / propagate / divide:_____

_____

_____

_____

Pests / problems:_____

_____

_____

_____

Notes:_____

_____

_____

_____

_____

_____

_____

_____

Photo / plant tag / seed packet / drawing:

Common name:_____

Botanical name:_____

Purchased at:_____ Price:_____

☐ Annual   ☐ Perennial   ☐ Flower   ☐ Shrub   ☐ Tree

☐ Bareroot   ☐ Groundcover   ☐ Fruit   ☐ Vegetable   ☐ Herb

Started from: ☐ Seed   ☐ Plant

Date germinated:_____ Date planted:_____

Location planted:_____

Planting instructions:_____

_____

_____

Sunlight: ☐ Full sun   ☐ Partial sun   ☐ Shade

Water requirements:_____ Size at maturity:_____

Care instructions:_____

_____

_____

_____

_____

Fertilizer / soil amendment / herbicide:_____

_____

_____

Harvest / bloom date:_____

Transplant / propagate / divide:_____

_____

_____

_____

Pests / problems:_____

_____

_____

_____

Notes:_____

_____

_____

_____

_____

_____

_____

_____

Photo / plant tag / seed packet / drawing:

Common name:_____

Botanical name:_____

Purchased at:_____ Price:_____

☐ Annual   ☐ Perennial   ☐ Flower   ☐ Shrub   ☐ Tree

☐ Bareroot   ☐ Groundcover   ☐ Fruit   ☐ Vegetable   ☐ Herb

Started from: ☐ Seed   ☐ Plant

Date germinated:_____ Date planted:_____

Location planted:_____

Planting instructions:_____

_____

_____

Sunlight: ☐ Full sun   ☐ Partial sun   ☐ Shade

Water requirements:_____ Size at maturity:_____

Care instructions:_____

_____

_____

_____

_____

Fertilizer / soil amendment / herbicide:_____

_____

_____

Harvest / bloom date:_____

Transplant / propagate / divide:_____

_____

_____

_____

Pests / problems:_____

_____

_____

_____

Notes:_____

_____

_____

_____

_____

_____

_____

_____

Photo / plant tag / seed packet / drawing:

Common name:_____

Botanical name:_____

Purchased at:_____ Price:_____

☐ Annual ☐ Perennial ☐ Flower ☐ Shrub ☐ Tree

☐ Bareroot ☐ Groundcover ☐ Fruit ☐ Vegetable ☐ Herb

Started from: ☐ Seed ☐ Plant

Date germinated:_____ Date planted:_____

Location planted:_____

Planting instructions:_____

_____

_____

Sunlight: ☐ Full sun ☐ Partial sun ☐ Shade

Water requirements:_____ Size at maturity:_____

Care instructions:_____

_____

_____

_____

_____

Fertilizer / soil amendment / herbicide:_____

_____

_____

Harvest / bloom date:_____

Transplant / propagate / divide:_____

_____

_____

_____

Pests / problems:_____

_____

_____

_____

© 1998 Journals Unlimited, Inc., Bay City, MI ™ "Write It Down" ® Series

Notes:_____

_____

_____

_____

_____

_____

_____

_____

_____

Photo / plant tag / seed packet / drawing:

Common name:_____

Botanical name:_____

Purchased at:_____ Price:_____

☐ Annual ☐ Perennial ☐ Flower ☐ Shrub ☐ Tree

☐ Bareroot ☐ Groundcover ☐ Fruit ☐ Vegetable ☐ Herb

Started from: ☐ Seed ☐ Plant

Date germinated:_____ Date planted:_____

Location planted:_____

Planting instructions:_____

_____

_____

Sunlight: ☐ Full sun ☐ Partial sun ☐ Shade

Water requirements:_____ Size at maturity:_____

Care instructions:_____

_____

_____

_____

Fertilizer / soil amendment / herbicide:_____

_____

_____

Harvest / bloom date:_____

Transplant / propagate / divide:_____

_____

_____

_____

Pests / problems:_____

_____

_____

_____

Notes:_____

_____

_____

_____

_____

_____

_____

_____

Photo / plant tag / seed packet / drawing:

Common name:_____

Botanical name:_____

Purchased at:_____ Price:_____

☐ Annual   ☐ Perennial   ☐ Flower   ☐ Shrub   ☐ Tree

☐ Bareroot   ☐ Groundcover   ☐ Fruit   ☐ Vegetable   ☐ Herb

Started from: ☐ Seed   ☐ Plant

Date germinated:_____ Date planted:_____

Location planted:_____

Planting instructions:_____

_____

_____

Sunlight: ☐ Full sun   ☐ Partial sun   ☐ Shade

Water requirements:_____ Size at maturity:_____

Care instructions:_____

_____

_____

_____

_____

Fertilizer / soil amendment / herbicide:_____

_____

_____

Harvest / bloom date:_____

Transplant / propagate / divide:_____

_____

_____

_____

Pests / problems:_____

_____

_____

_____

Notes:_____

_____

_____

_____

_____

_____

_____

_____

Photo / plant tag / seed packet / drawing:

Common name:_____

Botanical name:_____

Purchased at:_____ Price:_____

☐ Annual   ☐ Perennial   ☐ Flower   ☐ Shrub   ☐ Tree

☐ Bareroot   ☐ Groundcover   ☐ Fruit   ☐ Vegetable   ☐ Herb

Started from: ☐ Seed   ☐ Plant

Date germinated:_____ Date planted:_____

Location planted:_____

Planting instructions:_____

_____

_____

Sunlight: ☐ Full sun   ☐ Partial sun   ☐ Shade

Water requirements:_____ Size at maturity:_____

Care instructions:_____

_____

_____

_____

_____

Fertilizer / soil amendment / herbicide:_____

_____

_____

Harvest / bloom date:_____

Transplant / propagate / divide:_____

_____

_____

_____

Pests / problems:_____

_____

_____

_____

Notes:_____

_____

_____

_____

_____

_____

_____

_____

Photo / plant tag / seed packet / drawing:

Common name:_____

Botanical name:_____

Purchased at:_____ Price:_____

☐ Annual ☐ Perennial ☐ Flower ☐ Shrub ☐ Tree

☐ Bareroot ☐ Groundcover ☐ Fruit ☐ Vegetable ☐ Herb

Started from: ☐ Seed ☐ Plant

Date germinated:_____ Date planted:_____

Location planted:_____

Planting instructions:_____

_____

_____

Sunlight: ☐ Full sun ☐ Partial sun ☐ Shade

Water requirements:_____ Size at maturity:_____

Care instructions:_____

_____

_____

_____

_____

Fertilizer / soil amendment / herbicide:_____

_____

_____

Harvest / bloom date:_____

Transplant / propagate / divide:_____

_____

_____

_____

Pests / problems:_____

_____

_____

_____

Notes:_____

_____

_____

_____

_____

_____

_____

_____

_____

Photo / plant tag / seed packet / drawing:

Common name:_____

Botanical name:_____

Purchased at:_____ Price:_____

☐ Annual   ☐ Perennial   ☐ Flower   ☐ Shrub   ☐ Tree

☐ Bareroot   ☐ Groundcover   ☐ Fruit   ☐ Vegetable   ☐ Herb

Started from: ☐ Seed   ☐ Plant

Date germinated:_____ Date planted:_____

Location planted:_____

Planting instructions:_____

_____

_____

Sunlight: ☐ Full sun   ☐ Partial sun   ☐ Shade

Water requirements:_____ Size at maturity:_____

Care instructions:_____

_____

_____

_____

_____

Fertilizer / soil amendment / herbicide:_____

_____

_____

Harvest / bloom date:_____

Transplant / propagate / divide:_____

_____

_____

_____

Pests / problems:_____

_____

_____

_____

Notes:_____

_____

_____

_____

_____

_____

_____

_____

_____

Photo / plant tag / seed packet / drawing:

Common name:_____

Botanical name:_____

Purchased at:_____ Price:_____

☐ Annual   ☐ Perennial   ☐ Flower   ☐ Shrub   ☐ Tree

☐ Bareroot   ☐ Groundcover   ☐ Fruit   ☐ Vegetable   ☐ Herb

Started from: ☐ Seed   ☐ Plant

Date germinated:_____ Date planted:_____

Location planted:_____

Planting instructions:_____
_____
_____

Sunlight: ☐ Full sun   ☐ Partial sun   ☐ Shade

Water requirements:_____ Size at maturity:_____

Care instructions:_____
_____
_____
_____
_____

Fertilizer / soil amendment / herbicide:_____
_____
_____

Harvest / bloom date:_____

Transplant / propagate / divide:_____
_____
_____
_____

Pests / problems:_____
_____
_____
_____

Notes:_____

_____

_____

_____

_____

_____

_____

_____

_____

Photo / plant tag / seed packet / drawing:

Common name:_____

Botanical name:_____

Purchased at:_____ Price:_____

☐ Annual   ☐ Perennial   ☐ Flower   ☐ Shrub   ☐ Tree

☐ Bareroot   ☐ Groundcover   ☐ Fruit   ☐ Vegetable   ☐ Herb

Started from: ☐ Seed   ☐ Plant

Date germinated:_____ Date planted:_____

Location planted:_____

Planting instructions:_____

_____

_____

Sunlight: ☐ Full sun   ☐ Partial sun   ☐ Shade

Water requirements:_____ Size at maturity:_____

Care instructions:_____

_____

_____

_____

Fertilizer / soil amendment / herbicide:_____

_____

_____

Harvest / bloom date:_____

Transplant / propagate / divide:_____

_____

_____

Pests / problems:_____

_____

_____

_____

Notes:_____

_____

_____

_____

_____

_____

_____

_____

Photo / plant tag / seed packet / drawing:

Common name:_____

Botanical name:_____

Purchased at:_____ Price:_____

☐ Annual   ☐ Perennial   ☐ Flower   ☐ Shrub   ☐ Tree

☐ Bareroot   ☐ Groundcover   ☐ Fruit   ☐ Vegetable   ☐ Herb

Started from: ☐ Seed   ☐ Plant

Date germinated:_____ Date planted:_____

Location planted:_____

Planting instructions:_____

_____

_____

Sunlight: ☐ Full sun   ☐ Partial sun   ☐ Shade

Water requirements:_____ Size at maturity:_____

Care instructions:_____

_____

_____

_____

_____

Fertilizer / soil amendment / herbicide:_____

_____

_____

Harvest / bloom date:_____

Transplant / propagate / divide:_____

_____

_____

_____

Pests / problems:_____

_____

_____

_____

Notes:_____

_____

_____

_____

_____

_____

_____

_____

_____

Photo / plant tag / seed packet / drawing:

Common name:_____

Botanical name:_____

Purchased at:_____ Price:_____

☐ Annual ☐ Perennial ☐ Flower ☐ Shrub ☐ Tree

☐ Bareroot ☐ Groundcover ☐ Fruit ☐ Vegetable ☐ Herb

Started from: ☐ Seed ☐ Plant

Date germinated:_____ Date planted:_____

Location planted:_____

Planting instructions:_____

_____

_____

Sunlight: ☐ Full sun ☐ Partial sun ☐ Shade

Water requirements:_____ Size at maturity:_____

Care instructions:_____

_____

_____

_____

_____

Fertilizer / soil amendment / herbicide:_____

_____

_____

Harvest / bloom date:_____

Transplant / propagate / divide:_____

_____

_____

_____

Pests / problems:_____

_____

_____

_____

Notes:_____

_____

_____

_____

_____

_____

_____

_____

Photo / plant tag / seed packet / drawing:

Common name:_____

Botanical name:_____

Purchased at:_____ Price:_____

☐ Annual   ☐ Perennial   ☐ Flower   ☐ Shrub   ☐ Tree

☐ Bareroot   ☐ Groundcover   ☐ Fruit   ☐ Vegetable   ☐ Herb

Started from: ☐ Seed   ☐ Plant

Date germinated:_____ Date planted:_____

Location planted:_____

Planting instructions:_____

_____

_____

Sunlight: ☐ Full sun   ☐ Partial sun   ☐ Shade

Water requirements:_____ Size at maturity:_____

Care instructions:_____

_____

_____

_____

_____

Fertilizer / soil amendment / herbicide:_____

_____

_____

Harvest / bloom date:_____

Transplant / propagate / divide:_____

_____

_____

_____

Pests / problems:_____

_____

_____

_____

Notes:_____

_____

_____

_____

_____

_____

_____

_____

_____

Photo / plant tag / seed packet / drawing:

Common name:_____

Botanical name:_____

Purchased at:_____ Price:_____

☐ Annual   ☐ Perennial   ☐ Flower   ☐ Shrub   ☐ Tree

☐ Bareroot   ☐ Groundcover   ☐ Fruit   ☐ Vegetable   ☐ Herb

Started from: ☐ Seed   ☐ Plant

Date germinated:_____ Date planted:_____

Location planted:_____

Planting instructions:_____

_____

_____

Sunlight: ☐ Full sun   ☐ Partial sun   ☐ Shade

Water requirements:_____ Size at maturity:_____

Care instructions:_____

_____

_____

_____

_____

Fertilizer / soil amendment / herbicide:_____

_____

_____

Harvest / bloom date:_____

Transplant / propagate / divide:_____

_____

_____

_____

Pests / problems:_____

_____

_____

_____

Notes:_____

_____

_____

_____

_____

_____

_____

_____

Photo / plant tag / seed packet / drawing:

Common name:_____

Botanical name:_____

Purchased at:_____ Price:_____

☐ Annual ☐ Perennial ☐ Flower ☐ Shrub ☐ Tree

☐ Bareroot ☐ Groundcover ☐ Fruit ☐ Vegetable ☐ Herb

Started from: ☐ Seed ☐ Plant

Date germinated:_____ Date planted:_____

Location planted:_____

Planting instructions:_____

_____

_____

Sunlight: ☐ Full sun ☐ Partial sun ☐ Shade

Water requirements:_____ Size at maturity:_____

Care instructions:_____

_____

_____

_____

_____

Fertilizer / soil amendment / herbicide:_____

_____

_____

Harvest / bloom date:_____

Transplant / propagate / divide:_____

_____

_____

_____

Pests / problems:_____

_____

_____

_____

Notes:_____

_____

_____

_____

_____

_____

_____

_____

Photo / plant tag / seed packet / drawing:

Common name:_____

Botanical name:_____

Purchased at:_____ Price:_____

☐ Annual   ☐ Perennial   ☐ Flower   ☐ Shrub   ☐ Tree

☐ Bareroot   ☐ Groundcover   ☐ Fruit   ☐ Vegetable   ☐ Herb

Started from: ☐ Seed   ☐ Plant

Date germinated:_____ Date planted:_____

Location planted:_____

Planting instructions:_____

_____

_____

Sunlight: ☐ Full sun   ☐ Partial sun   ☐ Shade

Water requirements:_____ Size at maturity:_____

Care instructions:_____

_____

_____

_____

_____

Fertilizer / soil amendment / herbicide:_____

_____

_____

Harvest / bloom date:_____

Transplant / propagate / divide:_____

_____

_____

Pests / problems:_____

_____

_____

_____

Notes:_____

_____

_____

_____

_____

_____

_____

_____

_____

Photo / plant tag / seed packet / drawing:

Common name:_____

Botanical name:_____

Purchased at:_____ Price:_____

☐ Annual   ☐ Perennial   ☐ Flower   ☐ Shrub   ☐ Tree

☐ Bareroot   ☐ Groundcover   ☐ Fruit   ☐ Vegetable   ☐ Herb

Started from: ☐ Seed   ☐ Plant

Date germinated:_____ Date planted:_____

Location planted:_____

Planting instructions:_____

_____

_____

Sunlight: ☐ Full sun   ☐ Partial sun   ☐ Shade

Water requirements:_____ Size at maturity:_____

Care instructions:_____

_____

_____

_____

_____

Fertilizer / soil amendment / herbicide:_____

_____

_____

Harvest / bloom date:_____

Transplant / propagate / divide:_____

_____

_____

_____

Pests / problems:_____

_____

_____

_____

Notes:_____

_____

_____

_____

_____

_____

_____

_____

Photo / plant tag / seed packet / drawing:

Common name:_____

Botanical name:_____

Purchased at:_____ Price:_____

☐ Annual   ☐ Perennial   ☐ Flower   ☐ Shrub   ☐ Tree

☐ Bareroot   ☐ Groundcover   ☐ Fruit   ☐ Vegetable   ☐ Herb

Started from: ☐ Seed   ☐ Plant

Date germinated:_____ Date planted:_____

Location planted:_____

Planting instructions:_____

_____

_____

Sunlight: ☐ Full sun   ☐ Partial sun   ☐ Shade

Water requirements:_____ Size at maturity:_____

Care instructions:_____

_____

_____

_____

Fertilizer / soil amendment / herbicide:_____

_____

_____

Harvest / bloom date:_____

Transplant / propagate / divide:_____

_____

_____

_____

Pests / problems:_____

_____

_____

_____

Notes:_____

_____

_____

_____

_____

_____

_____

_____

_____

Photo / plant tag / seed packet / drawing:

Common name:_____

Botanical name:_____

Purchased at:_____ Price:_____

☐ Annual ☐ Perennial ☐ Flower ☐ Shrub ☐ Tree

☐ Bareroot ☐ Groundcover ☐ Fruit ☐ Vegetable ☐ Herb

Started from: ☐ Seed ☐ Plant

Date germinated:_____ Date planted:_____

Location planted:_____

Planting instructions:_____

_____

_____

Sunlight: ☐ Full sun ☐ Partial sun ☐ Shade

Water requirements:_____ Size at maturity:_____

Care instructions:_____

_____

_____

_____

_____

Fertilizer / soil amendment / herbicide:_____

_____

_____

Harvest / bloom date:_____

Transplant / propagate / divide:_____

_____

_____

_____

Pests / problems:_____

_____

_____

_____

Notes:_____

_____

_____

_____

_____

_____

_____

_____

_____

Photo / plant tag / seed packet / drawing:

Common name:_____

Botanical name:_____

Purchased at:_____ Price:_____

☐ Annual ☐ Perennial ☐ Flower ☐ Shrub ☐ Tree

☐ Bareroot ☐ Groundcover ☐ Fruit ☐ Vegetable ☐ Herb

Started from: ☐ Seed ☐ Plant

Date germinated:_____ Date planted:_____

Location planted:_____

Planting instructions:_____

_____

_____

Sunlight: ☐ Full sun ☐ Partial sun ☐ Shade

Water requirements:_____ Size at maturity:_____

Care instructions:_____

_____

_____

_____

_____

Fertilizer / soil amendment / herbicide:_____

_____

_____

Harvest / bloom date:_____

Transplant / propagate / divide:_____

_____

_____

_____

Pests / problems:_____

_____

_____

_____

Notes:_____

_____

_____

_____

_____

_____

_____

_____

Photo / plant tag / seed packet / drawing:

Common name:_____

Botanical name:_____

Purchased at:_____ Price:_____

☐ Annual ☐ Perennial ☐ Flower ☐ Shrub ☐ Tree

☐ Bareroot ☐ Groundcover ☐ Fruit ☐ Vegetable ☐ Herb

Started from: ☐ Seed ☐ Plant

Date germinated:_____ Date planted:_____

Location planted:_____

Planting instructions:_____

_____

_____

Sunlight: ☐ Full sun ☐ Partial sun ☐ Shade

Water requirements:_____ Size at maturity:_____

Care instructions:_____

_____

_____

_____

_____

Fertilizer / soil amendment / herbicide:_____

_____

_____

Harvest / bloom date:_____

Transplant / propagate / divide:_____

_____

_____

_____

Pests / problems:_____

_____

_____

_____

Notes:_____

_____

_____

_____

_____

_____

_____

_____

_____

Photo / plant tag / seed packet / drawing:

Common name:_____

Botanical name:_____

Purchased at:_____ Price:_____

☐ Annual ☐ Perennial ☐ Flower ☐ Shrub ☐ Tree

☐ Bareroot ☐ Groundcover ☐ Fruit ☐ Vegetable ☐ Herb

Started from: ☐ Seed ☐ Plant

Date germinated:_____ Date planted:_____

Location planted:_____

Planting instructions:_____

_____

_____

Sunlight: ☐ Full sun ☐ Partial sun ☐ Shade

Water requirements:_____ Size at maturity:_____

Care instructions:_____

_____

_____

_____

_____

Fertilizer / soil amendment / herbicide:_____

_____

_____

Harvest / bloom date:_____

Transplant / propagate / divide:_____

_____

_____

_____

Pests / problems:_____

_____

_____

_____

Notes:_____

_____

_____

_____

_____

_____

_____

_____

_____

Photo / plant tag / seed packet / drawing:

Common name:_____

Botanical name:_____

Purchased at:_____ Price:_____

☐ Annual ☐ Perennial ☐ Flower ☐ Shrub ☐ Tree

☐ Bareroot ☐ Groundcover ☐ Fruit ☐ Vegetable ☐ Herb

Started from: ☐ Seed ☐ Plant

Date germinated:_____ Date planted:_____

Location planted:_____

Planting instructions:_____

_____

_____

Sunlight: ☐ Full sun ☐ Partial sun ☐ Shade

Water requirements:_____ Size at maturity:_____

Care instructions:_____

_____

_____

_____

_____

Fertilizer / soil amendment / herbicide:_____

_____

_____

Harvest / bloom date:_____

Transplant / propagate / divide:_____

_____

_____

_____

Pests / problems:_____

_____

_____

_____

Notes:_____

_____

_____

_____

_____

_____

_____

_____

_____

Photo / plant tag / seed packet / drawing:

Common name:_____

Botanical name:_____

Purchased at:_____ Price:_____

☐ Annual ☐ Perennial ☐ Flower ☐ Shrub ☐ Tree

☐ Bareroot ☐ Groundcover ☐ Fruit ☐ Vegetable ☐ Herb

Started from: ☐ Seed ☐ Plant

Date germinated:_____ Date planted:_____

Location planted:_____

Planting instructions:_____

_____

_____

Sunlight: ☐ Full sun ☐ Partial sun ☐ Shade

Water requirements:_____ Size at maturity:_____

Care instructions:_____

_____

_____

_____

_____

Fertilizer / soil amendment / herbicide:_____

_____

_____

Harvest / bloom date:_____

Transplant / propagate / divide:_____

_____

_____

Pests / problems:_____

_____

_____

_____

Notes:_____

_____

_____

_____

_____

_____

_____

_____

Photo / plant tag / seed packet / drawing:

Common name:_____

Botanical name:_____

Purchased at:_____ Price:_____

☐ Annual ☐ Perennial ☐ Flower ☐ Shrub ☐ Tree

☐ Bareroot ☐ Groundcover ☐ Fruit ☐ Vegetable ☐ Herb

Started from: ☐ Seed ☐ Plant

Date germinated:_____ Date planted:_____

Location planted:_____

Planting instructions:_____

_____

_____

Sunlight: ☐ Full sun ☐ Partial sun ☐ Shade

Water requirements:_____ Size at maturity:_____

Care instructions:_____

_____

_____

_____

_____

Fertilizer / soil amendment / herbicide:_____

_____

_____

Harvest / bloom date:_____

Transplant / propagate / divide:_____

_____

_____

_____

Pests / problems:_____

_____

_____

_____

Notes:_____

_____

_____

_____

_____

_____

_____

_____

Photo / plant tag / seed packet / drawing:

Common name:_____

Botanical name:_____

Purchased at:_____ Price:_____

☐ Annual ☐ Perennial ☐ Flower ☐ Shrub ☐ Tree

☐ Bareroot ☐ Groundcover ☐ Fruit ☐ Vegetable ☐ Herb

Started from: ☐ Seed ☐ Plant

Date germinated:_____ Date planted:_____

Location planted:_____

Planting instructions:_____

_____

_____

_____

Sunlight: ☐ Full sun ☐ Partial sun ☐ Shade

Water requirements:_____ Size at maturity:_____

Care instructions:_____

_____

_____

_____

_____

Fertilizer / soil amendment / herbicide:_____

_____

_____

Harvest / bloom date:_____

Transplant / propagate / divide:_____

_____

_____

Pests / problems:_____

_____

_____

_____

Notes:_____

_____

_____

_____

_____

_____

_____

_____

_____

Photo / plant tag / seed packet / drawing:

Common name:_____

Botanical name:_____

Purchased at:_____ Price:_____

☐ Annual   ☐ Perennial   ☐ Flower   ☐ Shrub   ☐ Tree

☐ Bareroot   ☐ Groundcover   ☐ Fruit   ☐ Vegetable   ☐ Herb

Started from: ☐ Seed   ☐ Plant

Date germinated:_____ Date planted:_____

Location planted:_____

Planting instructions:_____

_____

_____

Sunlight: ☐ Full sun   ☐ Partial sun   ☐ Shade

Water requirements:_____ Size at maturity:_____

Care instructions:_____

_____

_____

_____

_____

Fertilizer / soil amendment / herbicide:_____

_____

_____

Harvest / bloom date:_____

Transplant / propagate / divide:_____

_____

_____

_____

Pests / problems:_____

_____

_____

_____

Notes:_____

_____

_____

_____

_____

_____

_____

_____

_____

Photo / plant tag / seed packet / drawing:

Common name:_____

Botanical name:_____

Purchased at:_____ Price:_____

☐ Annual   ☐ Perennial   ☐ Flower   ☐ Shrub   ☐ Tree

☐ Bareroot   ☐ Groundcover   ☐ Fruit   ☐ Vegetable   ☐ Herb

Started from: ☐ Seed   ☐ Plant

Date germinated:_____ Date planted:_____

Location planted:_____

Planting instructions:_____

_____

_____

Sunlight: ☐ Full sun   ☐ Partial sun   ☐ Shade

Water requirements:_____ Size at maturity:_____

Care instructions:_____

_____

_____

_____

_____

_____

Fertilizer / soil amendment / herbicide:_____

_____

_____

Harvest / bloom date:_____

Transplant / propagate / divide:_____

_____

_____

_____

Pests / problems:_____

_____

_____

_____

Notes:_____

_____

_____

_____

_____

_____

_____

_____

_____

Photo / plant tag / seed packet / drawing:

Common name:_____

Botanical name:_____

Purchased at:_____ Price:_____

☐ Annual   ☐ Perennial   ☐ Flower   ☐ Shrub   ☐ Tree

☐ Bareroot   ☐ Groundcover   ☐ Fruit   ☐ Vegetable   ☐ Herb

Started from: ☐ Seed   ☐ Plant

Date germinated:_____ Date planted:_____

Location planted:_____

Planting instructions:_____

_____

_____

_____

Sunlight: ☐ Full sun   ☐ Partial sun   ☐ Shade

Water requirements:_____ Size at maturity:_____

Care instructions:_____

_____

_____

_____

_____

Fertilizer / soil amendment / herbicide:_____

_____

_____

Harvest / bloom date:_____

Transplant / propagate / divide:_____

_____

_____

_____

Pests / problems:_____

_____

_____

_____

Notes:_____

_____

_____

_____

_____

_____

_____

_____

_____

Photo / plant tag / seed packet / drawing:

Common name:_____

Botanical name:_____

Purchased at:_____ Price:_____

☐ Annual   ☐ Perennial   ☐ Flower   ☐ Shrub   ☐ Tree

☐ Bareroot   ☐ Groundcover   ☐ Fruit   ☐ Vegetable   ☐ Herb

Started from: ☐ Seed   ☐ Plant

Date germinated:_____ Date planted:_____

Location planted:_____

Planting instructions:_____

_____

_____

Sunlight: ☐ Full sun   ☐ Partial sun   ☐ Shade

Water requirements:_____ Size at maturity:_____

Care instructions:_____

_____

_____

_____

_____

Fertilizer / soil amendment / herbicide:_____

_____

_____

Harvest / bloom date:_____

Transplant / propagate / divide:_____

_____

_____

_____

Pests / problems:_____

_____

_____

_____

Notes:_____

_____

_____

_____

_____

_____

_____

_____

Photo / plant tag / seed packet / drawing:

Common name:_____

Botanical name:_____

Purchased at:_____ Price:_____

☐ Annual   ☐ Perennial   ☐ Flower   ☐ Shrub   ☐ Tree

☐ Bareroot   ☐ Groundcover   ☐ Fruit   ☐ Vegetable   ☐ Herb

Started from: ☐ Seed   ☐ Plant

Date germinated:_____ Date planted:_____

Location planted:_____

Planting instructions:_____

_____

_____

Sunlight: ☐ Full sun   ☐ Partial sun   ☐ Shade

Water requirements:_____ Size at maturity:_____

Care instructions:_____

_____

_____

_____

_____

Fertilizer / soil amendment / herbicide:_____

_____

_____

Harvest / bloom date:_____

Transplant / propagate / divide:_____

_____

_____

_____

Pests / problems:_____

_____

_____

_____

Notes:_____

_____

_____

_____

_____

_____

_____

_____

_____

Photo / plant tag / seed packet / drawing:

Common name:_____

Botanical name:_____

Purchased at:_____ Price:_____

☐ Annual ☐ Perennial ☐ Flower ☐ Shrub ☐ Tree

☐ Bareroot ☐ Groundcover ☐ Fruit ☐ Vegetable ☐ Herb

Started from: ☐ Seed ☐ Plant

Date germinated:_____ Date planted:_____

Location planted:_____

Planting instructions:_____

_____

_____

Sunlight: ☐ Full sun ☐ Partial sun ☐ Shade

Water requirements:_____ Size at maturity:_____

Care instructions:_____

_____

_____

_____

_____

Fertilizer / soil amendment / herbicide:_____

_____

_____

Harvest / bloom date:_____

Transplant / propagate / divide:_____

_____

_____

Pests / problems:_____

_____

_____

_____

Notes:_____

_____

_____

_____

_____

_____

_____

_____

_____

Photo / plant tag / seed packet / drawing:

Common name:_____

Botanical name:_____

Purchased at:_____ Price:_____

☐ Annual ☐ Perennial ☐ Flower ☐ Shrub ☐ Tree

☐ Bareroot ☐ Groundcover ☐ Fruit ☐ Vegetable ☐ Herb

Started from: ☐ Seed ☐ Plant

Date germinated:_____ Date planted:_____

Location planted:_____

Planting instructions:_____

_____

_____

Sunlight: ☐ Full sun ☐ Partial sun ☐ Shade

Water requirements:_____ Size at maturity:_____

Care instructions:_____

_____

_____

_____

_____

Fertilizer / soil amendment / herbicide:_____

_____

_____

Harvest / bloom date:_____

Transplant / propagate / divide:_____

_____

_____

_____

Pests / problems:_____

_____

_____

_____

Notes:_____

_____

_____

_____

_____

_____

_____

_____

Photo / plant tag / seed packet / drawing:

Common name:_____

Botanical name:_____

Purchased at:_____ Price:_____

☐ Annual   ☐ Perennial   ☐ Flower   ☐ Shrub   ☐ Tree

☐ Bareroot   ☐ Groundcover   ☐ Fruit   ☐ Vegetable   ☐ Herb

Started from: ☐ Seed   ☐ Plant

Date germinated:_____ Date planted:_____

Location planted:_____

Planting instructions:_____

_____

_____

Sunlight: ☐ Full sun   ☐ Partial sun   ☐ Shade

Water requirements:_____ Size at maturity:_____

Care instructions:_____

_____

_____

_____

_____

Fertilizer / soil amendment / herbicide:_____

_____

_____

Harvest / bloom date:_____

Transplant / propagate / divide:_____

_____

_____

Pests / problems:_____

_____

_____

_____

Notes:_____

_____

_____

_____

_____

_____

_____

_____

_____

Photo / plant tag / seed packet / drawing:

Common name:_____

Botanical name:_____

Purchased at:_____ Price:_____

☐ Annual   ☐ Perennial   ☐ Flower   ☐ Shrub   ☐ Tree

☐ Bareroot   ☐ Groundcover   ☐ Fruit   ☐ Vegetable   ☐ Herb

Started from: ☐ Seed   ☐ Plant

Date germinated:_____ Date planted:_____

Location planted:_____

Planting instructions:_____

_____

_____

Sunlight: ☐ Full sun   ☐ Partial sun   ☐ Shade

Water requirements:_____ Size at maturity:_____

Care instructions:_____

_____

_____

_____

_____

Fertilizer / soil amendment / herbicide:_____

_____

_____

Harvest / bloom date:_____

Transplant / propagate / divide:_____

_____

_____

_____

Pests / problems:_____

_____

_____

_____

Notes:_____

_____

_____

_____

_____

_____

_____

_____

Photo / plant tag / seed packet / drawing:

Common name:_____

Botanical name:_____

Purchased at:_____ Price:_____

☐ Annual   ☐ Perennial   ☐ Flower   ☐ Shrub   ☐ Tree

☐ Bareroot   ☐ Groundcover   ☐ Fruit   ☐ Vegetable   ☐ Herb

Started from: ☐ Seed   ☐ Plant

Date germinated:_____ Date planted:_____

Location planted:_____

Planting instructions:_____

_____

_____

Sunlight: ☐ Full sun   ☐ Partial sun   ☐ Shade

Water requirements:_____ Size at maturity:_____

Care instructions:_____

_____

_____

_____

_____

Fertilizer / soil amendment / herbicide:_____

_____

_____

Harvest / bloom date:_____

Transplant / propagate / divide:_____

_____

_____

_____

Pests / problems:_____

_____

_____

Notes:_____

_____

_____

_____

_____

_____

_____

_____

_____

Photo / plant tag / seed packet / drawing:

Common name:_____

Botanical name:_____

Purchased at:_____ Price:_____

☐ Annual　　☐ Perennial　　☐ Flower　　☐ Shrub　　☐ Tree

☐ Bareroot　☐ Groundcover　☐ Fruit　　☐ Vegetable　☐ Herb

Started from: ☐ Seed　☐ Plant

Date germinated:_____ Date planted:_____

Location planted:_____

Planting instructions:_____

_____

_____

Sunlight: ☐ Full sun　☐ Partial sun　☐ Shade

Water requirements:_____ Size at maturity:_____

Care instructions:_____

_____

_____

_____

_____

Fertilizer / soil amendment / herbicide:_____

_____

_____

Harvest / bloom date:_____

Transplant / propagate / divide:_____

_____

_____

_____

Pests / problems:_____

_____

_____

Notes:_____

_____

_____

_____

_____

_____

_____

_____

Photo / plant tag / seed packet / drawing:

Common name:_____

Botanical name:_____

Purchased at:_____ Price:_____

☐ Annual ☐ Perennial ☐ Flower ☐ Shrub ☐ Tree

☐ Bareroot ☐ Groundcover ☐ Fruit ☐ Vegetable ☐ Herb

Started from: ☐ Seed ☐ Plant

Date germinated:_____ Date planted:_____

Location planted:_____

Planting instructions:_____

_____

_____

Sunlight: ☐ Full sun ☐ Partial sun ☐ Shade

Water requirements:_____ Size at maturity:_____

Care instructions:_____

_____

_____

_____

_____

Fertilizer / soil amendment / herbicide:_____

_____

_____

Harvest / bloom date:_____

Transplant / propagate / divide:_____

_____

_____

_____

Pests / problems:_____

_____

_____

_____

Notes:_____

_____

_____

_____

_____

_____

_____

_____

_____

Photo / plant tag / seed packet / drawing:

Common name:_____

Botanical name:_____

Purchased at:_____ Price:_____

☐ Annual   ☐ Perennial   ☐ Flower   ☐ Shrub   ☐ Tree

☐ Bareroot   ☐ Groundcover   ☐ Fruit   ☐ Vegetable   ☐ Herb

Started from: ☐ Seed   ☐ Plant

Date germinated:_____ Date planted:_____

Location planted:_____

Planting instructions:_____

_____

_____

Sunlight: ☐ Full sun   ☐ Partial sun   ☐ Shade

Water requirements:_____ Size at maturity:_____

Care instructions:_____

_____

_____

_____

_____

Fertilizer / soil amendment / herbicide:_____

_____

_____

Harvest / bloom date:_____

Transplant / propagate / divide:_____

_____

_____

_____

Pests / problems:_____

_____

_____

_____

_____

Notes:_____

_____

_____

_____

_____

_____

_____

_____

Photo / plant tag / seed packet / drawing:

Common name:_____

Botanical name:_____

Purchased at:_____ Price:_____

☐ Annual ☐ Perennial ☐ Flower ☐ Shrub ☐ Tree

☐ Bareroot ☐ Groundcover ☐ Fruit ☐ Vegetable ☐ Herb

Started from: ☐ Seed ☐ Plant

Date germinated:_____ Date planted:_____

Location planted:_____

Planting instructions:_____

_____

_____

Sunlight: ☐ Full sun ☐ Partial sun ☐ Shade

Water requirements:_____ Size at maturity:_____

Care instructions:_____

_____

_____

_____

_____

Fertilizer / soil amendment / herbicide:_____

_____

_____

Harvest / bloom date:_____

Transplant / propagate / divide:_____

_____

_____

_____

Pests / problems:_____

_____

_____

_____

Notes:_____

_____

_____

_____

_____

_____

_____

_____

_____

Photo / plant tag / seed packet / drawing:

THE POSSIBILITIES ARE ENDLESS...

Personalize It!

Personalized journals make the perfect gift for every age and interest!

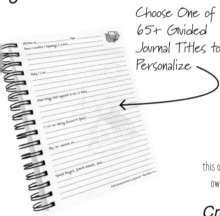

Choose One of 65+ Guided Journal Titles to Personalize

OPTION 1
Personalized Text

this option allows you to add your own text in a second window.

OPTION 2
Personalized Image

this option allows you to add your own special artwork or photo.

OPTION 3
Personalized Text & Image

this option allows you to add your own photo and your own text.

Create yours today at **JournalsUnlimited.com**

Make it Custom!

For quantities starting at 25

Perfect For:

- Corporate Gifts
- Company Promotions
- Conferences
- Special Events
- Gifts
- Retail Products
- Awards

3 *Sizes* AVAILABLE
- FULL
- MID
- MINI

2 *Cover* CHOICES
- KRAFT
- COLOR

Custom Design Department

Call for more information!

Toll Free: (800) 897-8528 • Phone: (989) 686-3377

EVERY JOURNAL TELLS A STORY...